Created and published by Knock Knock
1635-B Electric Avenue
Venice, CA 90291
knockknockstuff.com

Illustrations by Gemma Correll

ISBN: 978-160106677-0
UPC: 825703-50133-9

10 9 8 7 6 5 4 3 2

100 REASONS TO PANIC

ABOUT HAVING

A BABY

A JOURNAL FOR THE KNOCKED UP

KNOCK KNOCK®
VENICE, CALIFORNIA

#1. YOU CAN'T EVEN KEEP A PLANT ALIVE—HOW WILL YOU TAKE CARE OF A BABY?*

*Plants don't cry when they're hungry; babies do.

#2. PRIVACY WILL BECOME A FOREIGN CONCEPT. SO WILL FREEDOM.*

*Yes, but you won't be lonely (no matter how much you'd like to be).

DATE: _____/_____/_____

*If you'd.spent nine months cooped up in the same place,
you wouldn't look so hot yourself. It'll get cuter.

DATE: _____/_____/_____

#4. YOU WON'T BOND WITH YOUR NEWBORN.*

*You'll be together 24/7; with that much togetherness you could bond with a rock.

- -

#5. YOU'LL NEVER HAVE TIME TO READ ANYMORE.*

*You'll get to enjoy classics such as *How to Use This Rectal Thermometer*
and the back of the Children's Tylenol box.

DATE: _____/_____/_____

#6. YOU WON'T SURVIVE LABOR.*

*Think of all the nitwits who've pushed a baby out. You'll be okay.

DATE: _____/_____/_____

#7. YOU'LL NEVER SLEEP AGAIN.*

*That lack-of-sleep fog is just like being drunk without the pesky hangover.

DATE: _____/_____/_____

#8. ONCE YOU'RE A MOM, YOU'LL WEAR MOM JEANS.*

*The high elastic waist means you can eat whatever you want.

DATE: _____ / _____ / _____

#9. ONCE YOU'RE A DAD, YOU'LL WEAR DAD JEANS.*

*Dad jeans are better than bad genes.

DATE: _____/_____/_____

#10. NON-PARENT FRIENDS WON'T WANT TO HANG OUT
WITH YOU ANYMORE—BECAUSE YOU'RE BORING.*

*They'll die sad and alone.

DATE: _____/_____/_____

#11. YOU MIGHT BREAK THE BABY.*

*Babies are surprisingly durable.

DATE: _____/_____/_____

#12. YOU MIGHT BONK THE BABY'S HEAD ON A DOORFRAME.*

*You will do this at least once. Don't worry: see Reason 11.

#13. YOUR PARENTS AND IN-LAWS WILL BE OVERBEARING WITH THEIR ADVICE.*

*Your mutual desire to kill them will bring you and your partner closer.

DATE: _____/_____/_____

#14. DINNER OUT MEANS A 5:00 P.M. RESERVATION AT A "FAMILY-FRIENDLY" RESTAURANT.*

*Anything's better than cooking it yourself. You can also qualify for the early-bird special.

DATE: _____/_____/_____

DATE: _____/_____/_____

DATE: _____ / _____ / _____

#15. YOUR HOUSE WILL NEVER BE CLEAN.*

*Studies show that environmental dirt actually strengthens your baby's immune system.

#16. YOU'LL YELL AT YOUR KID.*

*If you don't, how will she learn to deal with mean bosses and coaches in the future?

#17. YOU'RE HAVING A BOY.*

*Someone will find your fart jokes funny.

#18. YOU'RE HAVING A GIRL.*

*Now you can read someone's diary!

#19. YOU'RE HAVING TWINS. OR—EEK—TRIPLETS.*

*At least your kids will always have a playmate.

#20. YOU WON'T BE ABLE TO STOP SWEARING, DAMN IT.*

*There's nothing funnier than a toddler with a potty mouth.

DATE: _____/_____/_____

#21. YOU CAN'T HIT THE BARS ANYMORE.*

*Drinking at home is cheaper.

#22. YOU'LL HAVE TO DO LAUNDRY ALL THE TIME.*

*At least you're not washing it on a rock in a river.

DATE: _____/_____/_____

#23. THE NAME YOU THOUGHT WAS SO UNIQUE WILL ROCKET TO POPULARITY.*

*When you go to amusement parks, she'll always be able
to find a personalized key chain and mug.

#24. THE NAME YOU THOUGHT WAS SO SPECIAL IS ACTUALLY JUST PLAIN WEIRD.*

*At least he'll always be able to get an email address with his name in it.

DATE: _____/_____/_____

#25. YOU'LL STOP TRAVELING TO FANTASTIC, FARAWAY DESTINATIONS.*

*You'll still get all the fun of packing— it will just be for a day
at the park, and will require more than a carry-on's worth of stuff.

DATE: _____/_____/_____

DATE: _____/_____/_____

#26. YOU'LL START DRIVING A KID-FRIENDLY CAR
LIKE A STATION WAGON, OR WORSE, THE DREADED MINIVAN.*

*Not worrying about spills and paint scratches is seriously liberating.

#27. YOUR KID WILL NEVER SHUT UP.*

*You'll tune out two-thirds of what she says.

DATE: _____/_____/_____

#28. YOU'RE TOO YOUNG TO HAVE A KID.*

*By the time your kid is out of the house, you'll just be hitting your prime.

#29. YOU'RE TOO OLD TO HAVE A KID.*

*You'll enjoy awkward moments with strangers while
they wonder if you're the haggard mom—or the hot granny.

DATE: _____ / _____ / _____

#30. YOU'LL NEVER SAVE ENOUGH TO SEND YOUR KID
TO COLLEGE—NO MATTER HOW MANY FANCY LATTES YOU FORGO.*

*Join the club.

#31. YOU'LL BECOME AN UNEMPLOYABLE HAS-BEEN WITH NO PROFESSIONAL RELEVANCE.*

*You can start a parenting blog and turn it into a bestseller.
Some successful bloggers are making up to seven figures a year.

DATE: _____ / _____ / _____

#32. ALL OF YOUR BAD HABITS WILL BE PASSED ON TO THIS LITTLE CREATURE.*

*So will all your good ones.

#33. YOU'LL HAVE TO SIT THROUGH INSIPID KIDS' MOVIES.*

*This is how you'll catch up on your sleep.

#34. ONE DAY, YOUR PRECIOUS BABY WILL REBEL AND COVER HIMSELF IN TATTOOS.*

*You'll be the person behind the "Mom" (or "Pop") inked on his chest.

DATE: _____ / _____ / _____

DATE: _____/_____/_____

DATE: _____/_____/_____

#35. YOU'LL GAIN A BOATLOAD OF PREGNANCY WEIGHT.*

*Oh, please. There's a whole other person inside there.

#36. YOUR KID WILL BE TRAUMATIZED BY DAYCARE.*

*Those teachers will probably be way more creative and patient than you.
If you're really lucky, they'll potty train your kid, too.

DATE: _____/_____/_____

#37. BABYSITTERS ARE EXPENSIVE.*

*You get to be the boss of someone other than the baby.

#38. YOUR WARDROBE BUDGET IS SURE TO SHRINK, IF NOT DISAPPEAR.*

*Baby clothes are really cute.

DATE: _____/_____/_____

#39. PEOPLE WITHOUT CHILDREN WILL THINK YOUR KID IS A SPOILED BRAT.*

*They're just empty-hearted and bitter.

#40. EVEN THE MOST COMPATIBLE COUPLES START TO FIGHT ONCE THEY HAVE A KID.*

*Dinner + couples therapy = date night.

#41. YOU'LL NEVER WEAR CASHMERE OR SILK AGAIN.*

*You'll save on dry cleaning.

DATE: _____/_____/_____

#42. YOU'LL HAVE TO ANSWER YOUR KID'S QUESTIONS ABOUT SEX.*

*Better he learns it from you than on the streets.

DATE: _____/_____/_____

#43. YOU'LL HAVE TO ANSWER YOUR KID'S QUESTIONS ABOUT GOD.*

*Better she learns it from you than on the streets.

#44. TOYS WiLL OVERTAKE YOUR LIFE—AND YOUR LIVING ROOM.*

*That Barbie Dream House you always coveted can now be yours.

#45. BABY POOP WILL MAKE YOU PUKE.*

*That's nothing that two days with a newborn won't solve.

DATE: _____/_____/_____

#46. YOU'LL HAVE TO ENDURE ENDLESS GAMES, MATCHES, MEETS, AND PRACTICES.*

*You're bound to find at least one kindred spirit among
all those annoying parents in the stands.

#47. YOUR BABY BOY WILL PEE ALL OVER YOU.*

*You'll develop astonishingly quick reflexes, and these reflexes
will come in handy for so many other needs.

#48. YOU'LL HUNGER FOR ADULT CONVERSATIONS.*

*You'll be able to tell a stegosaurus (spiked tail) from a triceratops (bony frill behind head).

#49. YOU WON'T BE ABLE TO CHANGE A DIAPER.*

*Have you ever assembled anything from IKEA? You'll be able to change a diaper.

DATE: _____/_____/_____

DATE: _____/_____/_____

DATE: _____/_____/_____

#50. BABY WEIGHT IS HARD TO LOSE.*

*Pediatricians say breastfeeding can burn 500
or more calories a day. Not breastfeeding? See Reason 66.

#51. YOUR KID WILL BE A TERRIBLY PICKY EATER.*

*More food for you.

#52. YOUR KID WILL HAVE CRAZY FOOD ALLERGIES.*

*Some people pay good money to be on gluten- and dairy-free diets.

#53. YOU'LL RUIN YOUR KID BY ALLOWING HER TO WATCH TOO MUCH TV.*

*The average child watches three to four hours of TV a day.
Shouldn't your kid be above average?

#54. YOU HAVE A DOG AND, FRANKLY, YOU NEVER TRAINED HIM WELL.
HOW WILL YOU REAR AN ACTUAL CHILD?*

*Everyone knows a dog, as well as your firstborn, is just a practice run.

DATE: _____/_____/_____

#55. YOU'LL DREAD CHANGING YOUR BABY'S DIAPERS AND FANTASIZE
ABOUT LETTING HER SIT IN IT.*

*If you're lucky, someday she'll change yours.

#56. YOU'LL WANT TO GO BACK TO WORK AND YOU'LL FEEL GUILTY.*

*You'll get to leave the house!

#57. YOU'LL WANT TO STAY HOME AND YOU'LL FEEL GUILTY.*

*You'll never have to leave the house!

#58. AFTER THE WHOLE BIRTHING EXPERIENCE, YOUR PARTNER WON'T LOOK AT YOU THE SAME WAY.*

*For a brief moment, you'll see each other as godlike beings.
After that, you'll both be too tired to notice each other at all.

DATE: _____/_____/_____

#59. YOUR KID WILL BE A BITER AND CHOMP ON OTHER PEOPLE'S CHILDREN.*

*What better way to weed the hypervigilant parents out of your life?

DATE: _____/_____/_____

#60. YOU'LL NEVER BATHE AGAIN.*

*You'll get quick and stealthy, like a bathing ninja.

#61. YOU'LL NEVER HAVE SEX AGAIN.*

*You'll get quick and stealthy, like a nookie ninja.

DATE: _____ / _____ / _____

#62. YOU'LL BE THAT PERSON WHO CONSTANTLY SHOWS
PHOTOS OF HIS KID TO STRANGERS.*

*You'll have an excuse to buy a fancy new camera.

#63. YOU'LL BE OBSESSED WITH READING PRODUCT LABELS
AND MAKING SURE EVERYTHING IS NONTOXIC.*

*Baby's first word will be "polyethylene terephthalate," a sure sign of genius.

DATE: _____/_____/_____

#64. ALONE TIME— WHAT'S THAT?*

*Going to the bathroom by yourself will feel more luxurious than a day at the spa.

DATE: _____/_____/_____

DATE: _____ / _____ / _____

#65. THE KID WILL RUIN YOUR NICE FURNITURE AND BREAK STUFF,
LIKE THAT PRICEY VINTAGE VASE YOU GOT AT AN ITALIAN FLEA MARKET.*

*You'll get to practice the Zen art of impermanence.

DATE: _____ / _____ / _____

#66. YOU WON'T HAVE TIME TO EXERCISE OR GO TO THE GYM.*

*Have you ever seen a toddler go? You'll get nothing but exercise.

#67. STRANGERS LIKE TO FONDLE A PREGNANT BELLY.*

*It's great prep for eighteen years of having your personal space invaded.

#68. YOU'LL HAVE TO PARTICIPATE IN DOZENS OF PLAY-DOH AND LEGO SESSIONS.*

*You'll find your inner child; it's in there somewhere.

DATE: _____ / _____ / _____

#69. ALL THE TODDLER FITS, MELTDOWNS, AND TANTRUMS WILL DRIVE YOU TO DRINK.*

*You'll be well prepared for adolescence.

#70. YOUR TEENAGER WILL HATE YOU.*

*She will, and then she won't, and then she will, and then she won't,
and then it will be the next day and you'll start all over again.

DATE: _____/_____/_____

#71. 80ing OUT TO EAT WiLL BE A NIGHTMARE.*

*You'll be amazed at how speedy the service will be.

#72. YOU'LL HAVE TO HELP YOUR KID WITH MATH HOMEWORK.*

*Maybe this time you'll get it.

DATE: _____/_____/_____

#73. YOUR SPOUSE WILL BE A LOUSY PARENT.*

*If it doesn't work out, at least you'll have the kid.

DATE: _____/_____/_____

#74. YOU'LL INVITE SCORN WHEN YOU GIVE UP ON CLOTH DIAPERS AND SWITCH TO DISPOSABLES.*

*Having a child increases your average lifetime carbon footprint by nearly six times, so it's sort of pointless worrying about cloth vs. disposables at all.

#75. DATE NIGHTS WILL BECOME A THING OF YORE.*

*Think of all the money you'll save on sushi, for Pete's sake. (Did someone say sake?)

DATE: _____/_____/_____

#76. YOU'LL LOSE TRACK OF YOUR TODDLER IN A CROWDED PUBLIC PLACE.*

*They usually only go far enough to give you a mild coronary.

#77. YOUR KID WILL BE A CONSERVATIVE.*

*You can embarrass him at rallies.

#78. YOUR KID WILL BE A LIBERAL.*

*You can embarrass her at rallies.

DATE: _____/_____/_____

#79. SOMETIMES YOUR BABY LOOKS KIND OF CREEPY, LiKE A MiNiATURE OLD MAN.*

*It's unlikely you'll be around when he's eighty, so it's your window into the future.

DATE: _____/_____/_____

DATE: _____ / _____ / _____

DATE: _____/_____/_____

#80. THAT FOOD FIGHT YOU NARROWLY ESCAPED IN HIGH SCHOOL
IS NOW MEALTIME AT YOUR HOUSE.*

*Scrubbing the floor tones your biceps and can burn up to 400 calories an hour.

#81. YOU'LL HAVE TO CHILDPROOF EVERYTHING.*

*That's impossible. Unless you have a giant plastic bubble.
And the giant plastic bubble is probably a suffocation risk.

DATE: _____/_____/_____

#82. YOUR KID WILL BE BULLIED.*

*Discovering your inner mama (or papa) bear is empowering.

DATE: _____/_____/_____

#83. YOUR KID WILL BE A BULLY.*

*Parents of bullies never worry about this.

DATE: _____/_____/_____

#84. YOUR BELOVED PET WON'T LIKE THE BABY.*

*When the kid starts dropping food on the floor they will become best friends.

DATE: _____/_____/_____

#85. YOUR KID WILL ASK QUESTIONS LIKE "WHY IS THE SKY BLUE?"
AND OTHER COUNTLESS CLASSICS YOU CAN'T ANSWER.*

*You will actually learn that the sky is blue because the wavelengths of blue
light passing through particles in the air are the right length to be most visible.

#86. YOU'LL SLIP UP ON THE SANTA SECRET.*

*There are undoubtedly worse secrets you could let slip.

#87. SHE'LL CRY AND YOU WON'T KNOW WHAT'S WRONG.*

*You won't have a clue what's wrong. But you'll figure out the wet cry,
the tired cry, and the hungry cry—eventually. Then you'll feel like the baby whisperer.

DATE: _____/_____/_____

#88. YOU'LL RAISE THE SCHOOL TROUBLEMAKER.*

*You'll develop really tight relationships with the principal and teachers.

DATE: _____/_____/_____

#89. PUBERTY WILL KILL YOU.*

*You survived it once, you'll survive it again; this time you won't have zits.

DATE: _____/_____/_____

#90. YOU WON'T LIKE YOUR KID'S FRIENDS.*

*Some days you'll like his friends more than you like him.

DATE: _____/_____/_____

DATE: _____/_____/_____

#92. YOU WON'T THINK YOUR KID IS CUTE (AKA "WHAT IF HE GETS GRANDPA'S NOSE?").*

*You're biologically preprogrammed to think they're cute.
This is what keeps you from selling them.

#93. THE BABY WILL BITE WHILE NURSING.*

*Only once: babies don't like it when you shriek and fling them from their food source.

#94. YOU'LL BECOME JUST LIKE THOSE PARENTS YOU USED TO MOCK.*

*If you do, you probably won't realize it.

DATE: _____/_____/_____

#95. YOU'LL FEEL GUILTY AT WORK ALL DAY LONG.*

*You'll feel guilty about everything as a parent. At least this one comes with a paycheck.

#96. YOU'LL CONSTANTLY COMPARE YOUR KID TO OTHERS, AND WORRY THAT HE'S NOT MEETING MILESTONES ON TIME.*

*Those babies who walk at six months will disappoint their parents in plenty of other ways later.

DATE: _____ / _____ / _____

#97. ROAD TRIPS WILL BE HELL.*

*This is why Twinkies, Cheetos, and handheld electronics exist.
You can bring some for the kids, too.

DATE: _____/_____/_____

#98. YOU'LL NEVER BE COOL AGAIN.*

*Your kid will think you're totally cool. Until middle school.

#99. YOU'LL BECOME JUST LIKE YOUR PARENTS.*

*Well, you turned out okay—in spite of all the mistakes those idiots made.

#100. YOU'LL SCREW YOUR KID UP, UTTERLY AND COMPLETELY.*

*You'll either keep her future therapist employed—
or be a major part of her memoir.

DATE: _____/_____/_____

DATE: _____/_____/_____

*DON'T WORRY.
IT'S WORTH IT.

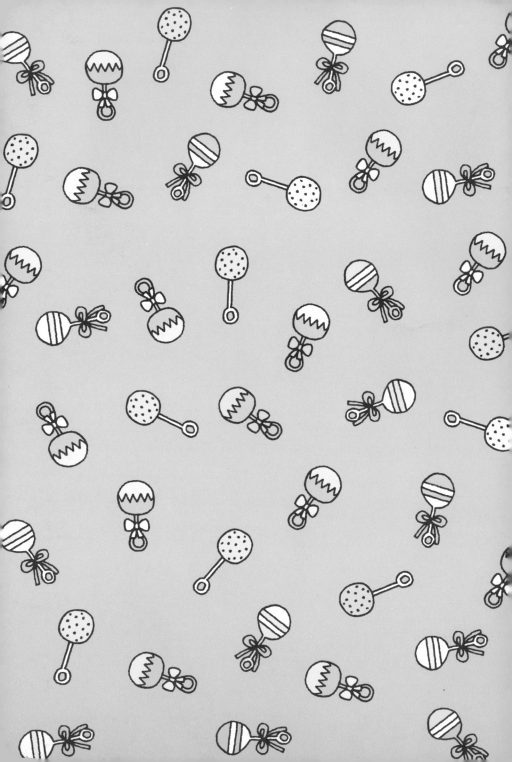